50 SIMPLE
L.E.D. CIRCUITS

by

R. N. SOAR

BERNARD BABANI (publishing) LTD
THE GRAMPIANS
SHEPHERDS BUSH ROAD
LONDON W6 7NF
ENGLAND

PLEASE NOTE

Although every care has been taken with the production of this book to ensure that any projects, information, designs, modifications and/or programs etc. contained herein, operate in a correct and safe manner and also that any components specified are normally available in Great Britain, the Publishers do not accept responsibility in any way for the failure, including fault in design, of any project, design, modification or program to work correctly or to cause damage to any other equipment that it may be connected to or used in conjunction with, or in respect of any other damage or injury that may be so caused, nor do the Publishers accept responsibility in any way for the failure to obtain specified components.

Notice is also given that if equipment that is still under warranty is modified in any way or used or connected with home-built equipment then that warranty may be void.

© 1977 BERNARD BABANI (publishing) LTD

ISBN 0 85934 043 0

First published — December 1977

Reprinted — April 1980

Reprinted — September 1982

Reprinted — January 1986

Printed and bound in Great Britain by Cox & Wyman Ltd, Readin

CONTENTS

INTRODUCTION

Light emitting diodes or LEDs are semiconductor devices made from materials such as gallium arsenide or gallium arsenide phosphide. The light is produced by electron/hole recombination when the diode is **UNDER FORWARD BIAS**, i.e. for light production the diode anode is positive with respect to the cathode. A current limiting resistor must always be included in series with the LED to control the current and prevent the LED from being damaged due to overheating. The light output increases with current but the current should not be allowed to exceed 20mA for a normal diode.

LEDs are now available in several colours — red, green, orange and yellow. The red LED is the most efficient, green LEDs require a much higher operating current for a comparable light output. Most of the circuits featured in this book are for red LEDs, as these are the most efficient and also cheaper than the other varieties.

Some of the circuits use red LEDs for voltage measurements, this depends on the constant voltage drop across a diode, green LEDs should not be substituted as the characteristics are very different. The circuits at the end of the book are for red LED seven segment common anode displays.

Various encapsulations are used for LEDs but the most common one has a cathode lead which is slightly longer than the anode lead. A flat on the encapsulation also indicates cathode.

Red LEDs are available in several sizes — 2mm, 3mm and 5mm. 5mm red LEDs were used in most of the prototype circuits.

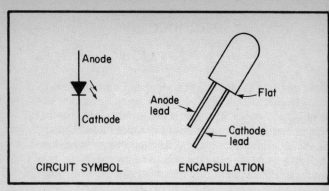

CIRCUIT SYMBOL   ENCAPSULATION

If the connection details of a LED are not known adopt the following procedure. Connect the LED **WITH A** 1KΩ **RESISTER IN SERIES** to a 9 volt battery, if the LED does not glow reverse connections. With the LED glowing the lead connected to the negative pole of the battery is the cathode.

CIRCUIT ONE

LED PILOT LIGHT

A LED makes a useful pilot light indicating that a piece of equipment is switched on. Most LEDs can be fitted with a plastic mounting bush, most retailers can supply these, so that the LED can be simply clipped into a hole drilled into the equipment front panel. Suitable values for the LED series resistor are shown in diagram (1). Green LEDs are much less efficient than red LEDs and so require a higher operating current and hence a lower value for the series resistor. The values shown give a reasonable brightness, if a very bright glow is required the values of resistance should be halved.

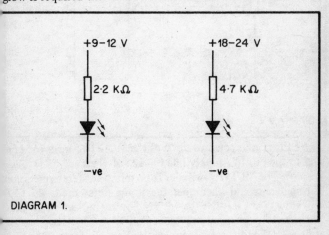

DIAGRAM 1.

CIRCUIT TWO

LED STEREO BEACON

A red LED makes an excellent stereo beacon for an I.C. stereo decoder such as the Motorola MC1310 or the Texas SN76115; the SN76115 is an exact replacement for the MC1310, the connection details are identical.

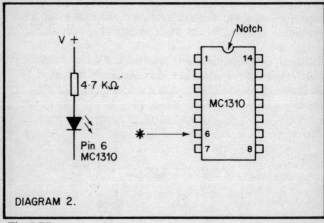

DIAGRAM 2.

The LED is connected to pin 6 of the MC1310 (or SN76115) and to the positive supply line (9–12 volts) via a 4.7KΩ ¼W resistor. The MC1310 switches from mono to stereo operation automatically and when operating in the stereo mode the LED will glow. The fact that the LED is glowing indicates that the phase lock loop circuit has 'locked on' to the 19KHz pilot tone it does NOT indicate stereo reception as such. Most stations continue to broadcast pilot tone during mono items especially on record shows. If the beacon is glowing but the sound is not stereo it is probably because the station is playing a mono record. If the beacon does not glow at all during a broadcast which is definitely stereo it is probably due to insufficient signal reaching the decoder. The MC1310 has a threshold level or stereo operation, if the signal level is very low the circuit will not switch over to stereo, this is likely if the receiver has an inadequate aerial. If the LED flickers this means that the MC1310 is switching rapidly between stereo and mono operation, this occurs when the 19KHz pilot tone input in a stereo signal is near to the threshold level, this is most likely to occur when trying to receive a distant station. The cure is to switch the decoder to mono operation, this is done by connecting pin 8 of the MC1310 to the negative line via a SPST switch (stereo defeat switch) when tuning in to a local station remember to switch it back to the normal-stereo position. If the flickering effect occurs with local station reception, this means that a better aerial must be used to obtain stereo reception.

A LED can be used with almost any stereo decoder which has a stereo beacon facility. In older decoders the LED and 4.7KΩ resistor can be wired in place of the stereo indicator bulb. If the decoder is positive earth (likely if PNP transistors used) the LED should be wired with the cathode connected to the negative supply voltage.

CIRCUIT THREE

STEREO DECODER MONO/STEREO INDICATOR

Circuit three is a further development of circuit two, here in addition to the stereo beacon a green LED is used to indicate mono operation, i.e. normal stereo operation has been defeated because the decoder is too noisy operating in the stereo mode, which may be the case when tuned to a distant stereo FM station.

When pin 8 of the MC1310 I.C. is earthed the stereo/mono switch is disabled and the decoder operates in mono only and the stereo beacon is switched off, but the green LED is now

connected to earth, completing the circuit, and glows to
indicate MONO operation.

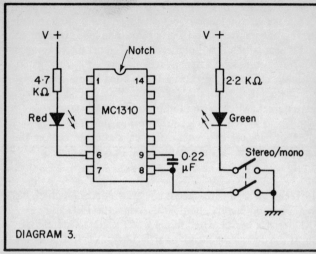

DIAGRAM 3.

In the diagram the components in the rest of the decoder
circuit are omitted for clarity. The stereo defeat switch is a
DPST type. One of the miniature DPDT slide switches can be
used, in this case the extra set of contacts are not connected.

CIRCUIT FOUR

SUBMINIATURE LED TORCH

This is a very simple circuit for a torch small enough to fit
into a matchbox, if miniature 1½v cells are used to power the
LED. The light given out by a red LED is not very bright but
it is sufficient to enable one to locate a keyhole, check change
in the darkness. The torch can be equipped with a sub-
miniature slide switch to enable it to be turned on and off.
No resistor is required in series with the LED as the applied
voltage is only 3 volts or less.

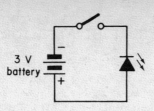

DIAGRAM 4.

CIRCUIT FIVE

LOW VOLTAGE LOW CURRENT SUPPLY

A LED can be used as a low voltage low current rectifier capable of supplying a few mA for a transistor circuit.

A LED as a rectifier has the advantage that it also functions as a power 'ON' indicator. The LED can be supplied from a low voltage winding such as a 6.3v heater transformer.

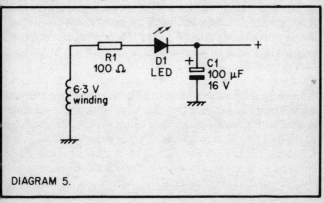

DIAGRAM 5.

CIRCUIT SIX

MICROLIGHT INDICATOR

A 2mm red LED can be used as a very low current indicator for transistorised equipment. A red LED will still produce a visible gleam from a 9 volt supply even when supplied via a 100KΩ resistor.

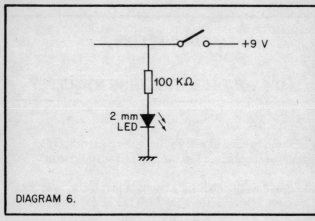

DIAGRAM 6.

Although the gleam from a LED at such a very low current is not very bright the transition from nonillumination to illumination when switched on is easily noticed and this is a very useful indication of switching a function e.g. to 'record' on a battery tape recorder.

A 2mm LED is easily fitted into a plastic cabinet by drilling a small hole and securing the LED with polystyrene cement, as used with plastic 'construction kits'.

CIRCUIT SEVEN

ULTRA LOW CURRENT
LED SWITCHING INDICATOR

This circuit uses a red LED to indicate that a circuit has been switched to a particular function, the LED is only required to glow for a few seconds for reliable indication and can then be extinguished. The basis of the circuit is that a capacitor is charged up by the battery supply and the capacitor supplies the current for the LED, once the capacitor is discharged the LED ceases to glow. The switches shown in the diagram (7) are ganged to the function switch, which could be the PLAY/RECORD switch fitted to a battery tape recorder.

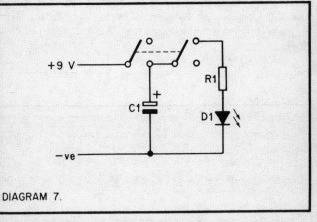

DIAGRAM 7.

The electrolytic capacitor charges up again when the circuit is switched back. The value of the resistor R1 controls the length the LED glow persists, a lower value can be used, this will give a brighter glow for a shorter time. If a higher value of R1 is used this produces a dimmer glow which persists longer.

Components List

C1   1000µF 16v electrolytic
R1   22KΩ ¼W
D1   RED LED
SWITCH 2 pole 2 way (part of function switch)

CIRCUIT EIGHT

LED STROBOSCOPE

This is a simple circuit which uses a red LED as a stroboscopic flash generator. The LED is powered from a 6.3v AC heater winding. The LED glows only when forward biased so that the LED is on for only half the AC cycle and so flashes 50 times per second when powered from AC with a frequency of 50Hz.

One common use is in conjunction with a stroboscopic record speed disc.

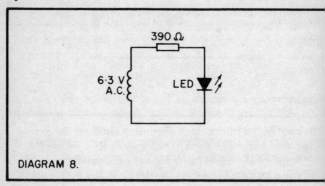

DIAGRAM 8.

CIRCUIT NINE

12 VOLT CAR CIRCUIT TESTER

This is a LED probe for testing 12 volt car wiring circuits. One lead of the tester is clipped to chassis, which forms the negative connection, the second lead is in the form of a probe. When the probe touches a connection at a potential of 12 volts with respect to chassis, the LED will glow brightly.

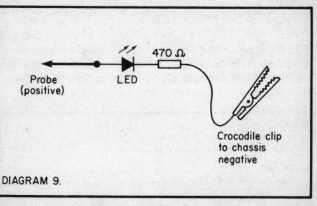

DIAGRAM 9.

If the tester is required for use with a positive chassis car the LED should be wired the other way round so that the anode is connected to the chassis (positive).

If a 2mm red LED is used for the tester, this together with a 470Ω ¼W resistor can be fitted inside an empty transparent ball-point pen tube, the negative lead can be a flying lead fitted with a crocodile clip. The probe can be a long screw or nail secured in the tube with polystyrene cement.

CIRCUIT TEN

TWO COLOUR LED

This is a circuit for the experimenter, the results vary between diodes. The circuit uses a green LED. A green LED is much less efficient at light production when operated at low current levels. A green LED glows bright green at a high current level but at a lower current level the glow degenerates to an orangey-red. If the series resistor used with a green LED is switched so as to alter the current flowing through the LED this is in effect a method of colour change. At a voltage of 9 volts a green LED glows green with a series resistor of 2.2KΩ and orange/red with a resistor of 22KΩ. The effect varies with diodes and the actual resistor values may require some adjustment for an optimum colour change.

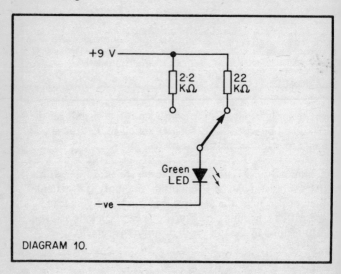

DIAGRAM 10.

CIRCUIT ELEVEN

12 VOLT CAR "FUSE BLOWN" INDICATOR

This is a simple indicator circuit for car use. The LED and its series resistor are wired across the car fuse. As long as the fuse is intact, the LED is shorted out and does not glow. If the fuse blows the current now passes through the LED and the LED glows to indicate "FUSE BLOWN". A small current flows into the car circuit via the LED but this is only a few mA.

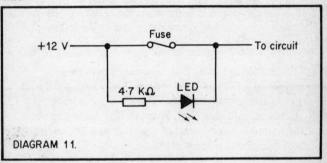

DIAGRAM 11.

CIRCUIT TWELVE

LED CONTINUITY TESTER

This is a simple continuity tester for testing wires for breaks, fuses, identifying wires when polarising loudspeakers, etc. The LED will glow very brightly for low resistance wiring but will still test quite high resistance circuits, although in this case the LED glow will be much dimmer.

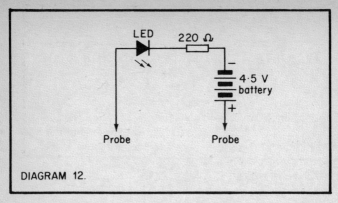

DIAGRAM 12.

One caution is that the users fingers should not be touching
the probes if the skin is slightly moist firm contact with the
probes will make the LED glow dimly due to a small current
flowing via the skin.

It is very useful for testing the fuses which have ceramic
tubes which make it impossible to see the fusewire, if the
LED glows bright — fuse alright! The 2 wires can be fitted
with probes or crocodile clips. When testing wires make sure
that the wires are not connected to any source of current,
only test equipment when it is off.

CIRCUIT THIRTEEN

LED CURRENT OVERLOAD INDICATOR

This is a very simple but useful circuit for indicating the current
flowing in a circuit. It may be of interest to teachers as a
simple demonstration of OHM's Law.

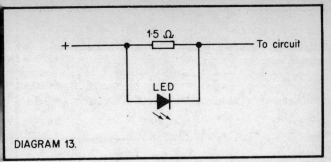

DIAGRAM 13.

The voltage drop across a red LED is about 1½ volts, i.e. there must be a voltage of about 1½ volts across a LED for it to glow. A red LED is connected in parallel with a 1.5Ω 3 watt wirewound resistor. The voltage drop across the resistor increases with increasing current, when the voltage drop exceeds 1.5 volts the LED will glow.

From OHM's Law

$$V = IR$$

If $V = 1.5$ volts
       $R = 1.5$ ohms
then $I = 1$ Amp

this means that if the current flowing through the resistor is greater than about 1 amp the LED glows.

If the circuit is used in conjunction with a power supply which can only normally supply up to 1 amp (e.g. model control supply unit) the LED functions as an overload (overLED!) indicator. The LED glows to indicate OVERLOAD, current in excess of 1 amp.

At heavy currents the resistor used is a very low resistance wirewound type of sufficient wattage rating to carry the circuit current.
The wattage rating is calculated from

$$W = I^2 R$$

where R is the resistance in ohms
I^2 is the square of the current flowing in amps

W is the wattage rating in watts

The circuit can easily be used for other current levels by altering the value of the resistor, lower current higher resistor value.

Example:

to indicate on a circuit current of 500mA, current $I = 0.5A$

$$V = 1.5 \text{ volts}$$
$$R = \frac{V}{I}$$
$$R = \frac{1.5}{0.5}$$
$$R = 3$$

nearest resistor value is 3.3
wattage rating is $I^2 R$

$$R = 3\Omega$$
$$I = 0.5$$
$$\therefore I^2 = 0.5 \times 0.5$$
$$= 0.25$$
$$W = 0.25 \times 3$$
$$W = 0.75$$

$\therefore$ a resistor of at least 1 watt rating must be used.

A green LED can be used but as the voltage drop across a green LED is about 2.2 volts the resistor values must be calculated accordingly.

CIRCUIT FOURTEEN

LED CURRENT RANGE INDICATOR

This is a development from circuit (13). The voltage drop across a silicon rectifier under forward bias is about 0.75 volts, the voltage drop across three silicon rectifiers in series is about

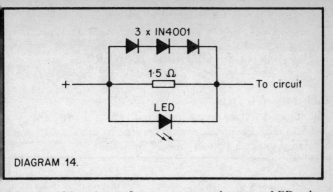

DIAGRAM 14.

2.2 volts. If 3 such rectifiers are connected across a LED, when the voltage exceeds 2.2 volts the rectifiers conduct and, due to their much smaller forward resistance, short out the LED and extinguish it. This means that when the current through the resistor produces a voltage drop in excess of 2.2 volts the LED is extinguished.

from OHM's Law

$$I = \frac{V}{R}$$

V is 2.2 volts

R is 1.5 ohms

$$I = \frac{2.2}{1.5}$$

I is about 1½ amps

so this means that the LED is extinguished when the current exceeds 1½ amps, the LED is extinguished when the current is below 1 amp. If the LED is glowing this indicates that the current flowing through the resistor is between 1 and 1½ amps.

The resistor in the diagram is a 1.5Ω 3 watt wirewound type, the rectifiers are type 1N4001 or similar (50v p.i.v. lamp rating). The current range indicated can be adjusted by altering the value of the resistor.

CIRCUIT FIFTEEN

1.5 VOLT LED "ZENER"

The forward voltage drop across a red LED is about 1½ volts
and so a red LED under forward bias can be used as a 1½ volt
reference source a 1½ volt "zener" equivalent.

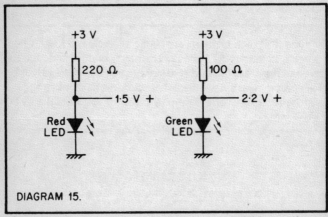

DIAGRAM 15.

This is very useful as zener diodes are not available in voltages
below 2.7V. The current through the LED must, as with a
zener diode, be limited by a resistor. If a 2.2 volt reference
source is required a green LED can be utilised. The LEDs are
under forward bias unlike a true zener diode which is reverse
biased for voltage regulation i.e. with cathode positive.

CIRCUIT SIXTEEN

EXTENDING ZENER VOLTAGE

A LED can be connected in series with a zener diode to
increase the reference voltage by 1½ volts for a red LED and
2.2 volts for a green LED. For example a 7.5 volt zener diode
in series with a red LED is equivalent to a 9 volt zener.

The LED has the advantage that it also functions as a pilot light.

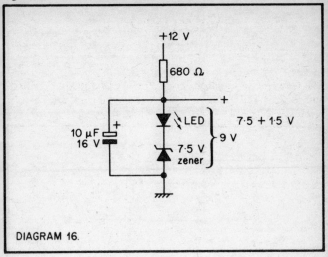

DIAGRAM 16.

CIRCUIT SEVENTEEN

FOUR VOLTAGE REGULATED SUPPLY

Four red LEDs in series can be utilised as a four voltage regulated supply 1½v, 3v, 4½v, 6 volt, equivalent to a battery supply with regard to the voltages available.

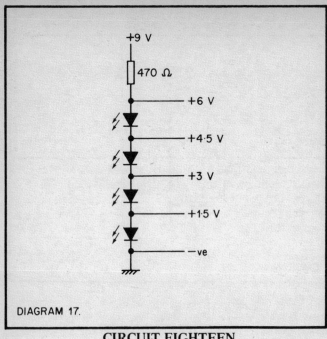

DIAGRAM 17.

CIRCUIT EIGHTEEN

PsychaLEDic Display

This is a very simple two red LED flashing light display which plugs into the earpiece socket of a small transistor radio. The LEDs are powered by the transistor radio audio output, and flash on and off in time to the music, the music itself can be heard on a second radio tuned to the same radio station. The two radios combine to give a sound and light display.

The volume control of the radio should be adjusted so that the LEDs glow dimly on quiet sounds as monitored on the second radio, the LEDs will then flash brightly on loud sounds.

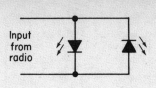

Input
from
radio

DIAGRAM 18.

For the best results the LEDs display should be viewed in a
darkened room, the effect is of gently pulsating light. The 2
LEDs can be mounted in front of 2 sheets of aluminium fixed
together at right angles, this arrangement gives multiple
images of the LEDs.

An alternative to the 2 sheets of aluminium is cooking foil
glued to sheets of cardboard.

The LED display should only be used with the output from
a small transistor radio, a large audio signal will overload the
LEDs and damage them.

CIRCUIT NINETEEN

DUAL COLOUR DISPLAY

A further development of circuit (18) is to use a red and a
green LED in the display. A green LED is much less sensitive
than a red LED so a 1N4001 silicon rectifier is connected in
series with the red LED in order to equalise the light outputs
of the 2 LEDs. The dual colour display will require a higher
audio operating current than circuit (18).

25

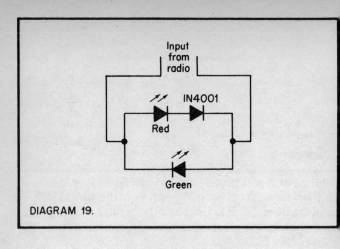

DIAGRAM 19.

CIRCUIT TWENTY

DUAL SIGNAL DEVICE

This is a simple 2 LED device which enables 2 wires to control 2 separate LED indicators. If 2 LEDs are connected in inverse parallel, as a LED only glows when under forward bias, the polarity of the voltage applied to the pair of LEDs determines which LED will glow.

The circuit is battery powered and a DPDT control switch reverses the connections to the battery. At position (i) LED 1 glows, at position (ii) LED 2 glows. As the two red LEDs are powered by a 3 volt battery, no limiting resistor is required. If a 2 pole 3 way switch is used the switches third position can be LEDs off.

26

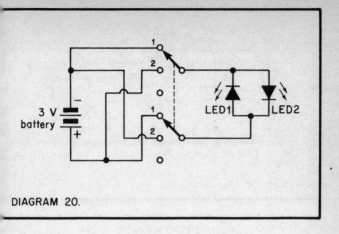

DIAGRAM 20.

CIRCUIT TWENTY-ONE

LED TRIPLE SIGNALLING

A further development of circuit (20) is possible if the circuit is powered by 2 volts AC derived from a low voltage mains transformer.

Two 1N4001 silicon rectifiers can be used to provide supplies of alternate polarity but a third position of switching, supplying the LEDs with AC means that both LEDs glow.

If a 1 pole 4 way switch is used the signal positions possible are

        (i)   LED 1 on.
        (ii)   LED 2 on.
        (iii)   LED 1 and LED 2 on.
        (iv)   LEDs off.

Thus a 2 wire circuit can carry 3 distinct signals.

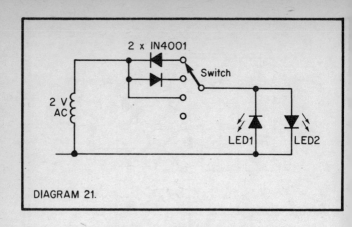

DIAGRAM 21.

CIRCUIT TWENTY-TWO

SUB-MINIATURE LIGHT SOURCE
FOR MODEL RAILWAYS

A 2mm LED is a minute light source ideal for building into locomotives on model railways to simulate firebox glow etc. The one disadvantage is that a LED is polarity conscious, if the supply to a locomotive is reversed to cause the locomotive to run in the opposite direction, the LED will be extinguished.

The solution is to build a miniature bridge rectifier inside the locomotive shell, powered by the locomotive supply. Such a bridge rectifier provides a constant supply for one or several LEDs regardless of polarity input to the bridge. Each 2mm LED used should be fitted with a 470Ω or greater value resistor

The bridge rectifier should be assembled from four 1N4001 silicon rectifiers, these are very small and should present no mounting problems. 2mm yellow LEDs would be suitable for mounting inside railway coaches to simulate coach lights.

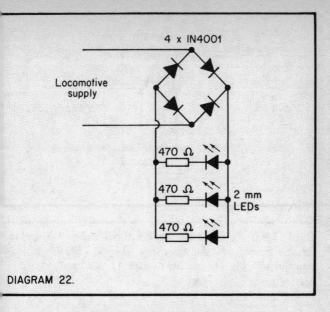

Locomotive
supply

4 x IN4001

470 Ω

470 Ω   2 mm
LEDs

470 Ω

DIAGRAM 22.

CIRCUIT TWENTY-THREE

PORTABLE TELEVISION PROTECTION CIRCUIT

This is a LED circuit for use with a 12 volt battery portable
television set. If a portable television is powered from a 12
volt car battery, the television can be damaged if the battery
polarity is incorrect.

In the circuit the 1N5400 rectifier will only conduct and pass
current to the circuit if the applied polarity is correct. If the
battery polarity is correct the red LED is reverse biased and
does not glow. If the battery polarity is incorrect the 1N5400
is reverse biased and will not conduct protecting the television
circuit from damage, the red LED is now forward biased and
will glow to indicate FAULT — battery reversed.

29

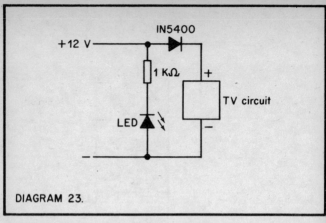

DIAGRAM 23.

The 1N5400 silicon rectifier specified is a 3 amp type and is suitable for any portable television. The red LED can be fitted into the portable TV case next to the 12 volt battery connector.

CIRCUIT TWENTY-FOUR

IMPROVED PORTABLE TV
PROTECTION CIRCUIT

A development of circuit (23), this circuit uses two LEDs, one red, one green.

The red LED glows only if the 12 volt battery polarity is wrong to indicate FAULT — battery reversed.

The green LED glows if the battery polarity is correct and indicates normal operation.

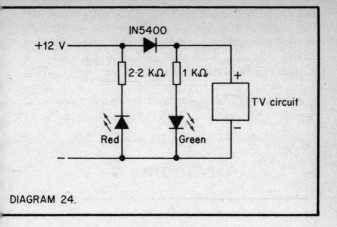

DIAGRAM 24.

CIRCUIT TWENTY-FIVE

LED BATTERY TESTER

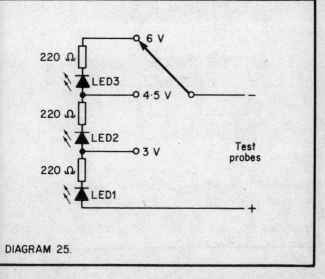

DIAGRAM 25.

This is a simple inexpensive GOOD/NO GOOD tester for 3v, 4½v or 6v batteries. The switch sets the tester to the various voltages. A 3 volt battery will make LED 1 glow, a 4½ volt battery will make LED 1 and LED 2 glow, a 6 volt battery will make LED1, LED 2 and LED 3 glow.

A substandard or failing battery will produce a dim or fading glow or no glow at all. The switch used is a 1 pole 3 way type.

CIRCUIT TWENTY-SIX

SIMPLE LED TIMER

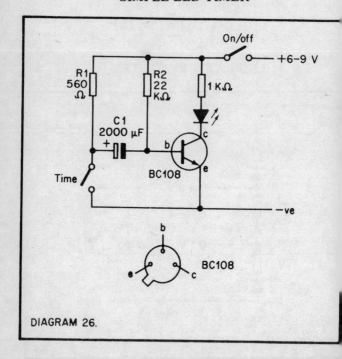

DIAGRAM 26.

his is a simple electronic timer, when the TIME button is
ressed the red LED is extinguished, about 30 seconds later
ie LED glows again to indicate time elapsed. The time
eriod depends on the value of C1, increasing the value of
1 extends the time period. The circuit can be powered by
to 9 volts.

omponents List

1	560Ω	
2	22KΩ	¼W
3	1KΩ	
1	2000µF 16V electrolytic	

ransistor silicon NPN BC108 or similar
ime switch SPST type

CIRCUIT TWENTY-SEVEN

LED LOGIC PROBE

his is a two LED Logic Probe which is powered by the 5 volt
rcuit supply under test.

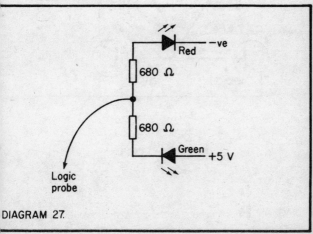

DIAGRAM 27.

33

When the probe is connected to the 5 volt supply both red and green LEDs will glow. When the logic probe touches a circuit connection, if the GREEN LED glows brightly this indicates logic level 0, if the RED LED glows brightly this indicates logic level 1.

CIRCUIT TWENTY-EIGHT

FLASHING LED DISPLAY

This is a two red LED flashing display based on the use of a low frequency transistor multivibrator circuit.

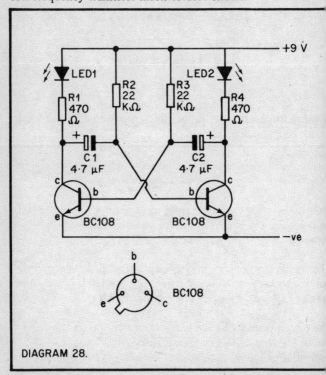

DIAGRAM 28.

he values indicated in the circuit diagram give a rapid on/off
isplay, if the value of C1 and C2 is increased this will give a
ower frequency and hence slower flashing rate.

omponents List

1	470Ω	⎤		C1	4.7µF 16V
2	22KΩ			C2	4.7µF 16V
3	22KΩ	¼W		LED1, LED2 red LEDs
4	470Ω	⎦			

r1, Tr2 BC108 or similar silicon NPN transistors

CIRCUIT TWENTY-NINE

EXPERIMENTAL UNIJUNCTION
LED FLASHER

his is a LED circuit for the experimenter.

he circuit is based on a very low frequency unijunction
scillator. The pulses of current through R3 produce a voltage
rhich causes the LED to flash.

he flashes occur at regular intervals, the time period depends
n the value of C1, which must be a non-electrolytic type
apacitor.

he flashes are not very bright, with some LEDs the flash may
nly be visible in a darkened room. The brilliance of the flash
aay be increased by using a supply of 18 volts.

he circuit depends on the low level current performance of
ie LED, if the LED is of poor efficiency which may be the
ase with low price "surplus" or "bargain" types, it will not
ork in this particular circuit. The interval between flashes

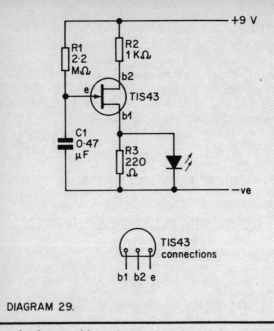

DIAGRAM 29.

can be decreased by reducing the value of C1 e.g. to 0.22µF or increased by using a higher value e.g. 1µF or 2.2µF.

Components List

R1   2.2MΩ ⎤
R2   1KΩ   ⎥ ¼W
R3   220Ω ⎦
C1   0.47uF
Unijunction transistor type T1S43 or UT46

36

CIRCUIT THIRTY

AUDIO FREQUENCY ZERO BEAT INDICATOR

If two AF oscillators are connected together and are very near in frequency a low frequency or beat frequency corresponding to the difference between the two frequencies is produced. When the two oscillators are at the same frequency the beat frequency is zero. If the resultant AF voltage is fed to two red LEDs in inverse parallel, as the beat frequency falls below 50Hz the LEDs will flicker at a slower and slower rate until at near zero beat both LEDs will be extinguished indicating that the 2 oscillators are operating at the same frequency.

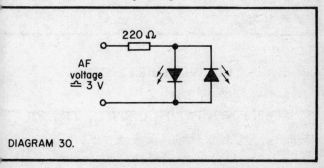

DIAGRAM 30.

CIRCUIT THIRTY-ONE

SIMPLE TRANSISTOR TESTER

This is a very simple GOOD/NO GOOD tester for small signal NPN transistors. If the transistor is good the LED will glow brightly.

The circuit only tests the ability of a transistor as a current amplifier.

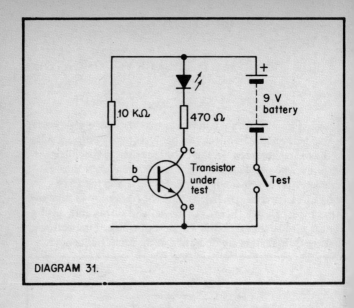

DIAGRAM 31.

CIRCUIT THIRTY-TWO

SIMPLE NPN/PNP TRANSISTOR TESTER

This is a development from circuit (31) by switching the battery connections to reverse the polarity and using two red LEDs of alternate polarity the tester now caters for both NPN and PNP transistors.

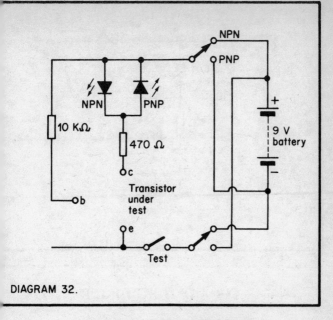

DIAGRAM 32.

CIRCUIT THIRTY-THREE

VERY LOW CURRENT LED
ON/OFF INDICATOR

This is an on/off indicator for battery powered equipment, the circuit only uses power for a few seconds after switching on.

At switch on C1 charges via R1 and LED 1, LED 1 glows to indicate ON, the glow rapidly fades away as C1 charges up, when C1 is fully charged the LED ceases to glow as no current is flowing. At switch OFF, C1 discharges via R1 and LED 2, and LED 2 glows to indicate OFF, discharging C1.

39

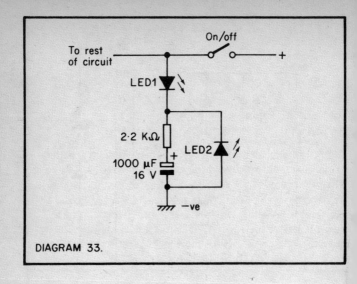

DIAGRAM 33.

CIRCUIT THIRTY-FOUR

BINARY DEMONSTRATOR

This is a circuit to demonstrate the fundamental idea of the binary system of numbers.

A 6 way switch turns on 3 red LEDs in turn to correspond with the denary (base 10) numbers 1–6.

LED 1 indicates 2^0 (= 1)
LED 2 indicates 2^1 (= 2)
LED 3 indicates 2^2 (= 4)

Counting is

DENARY	BINARY
1	1
2	1 0
3	1 1
4	1 0 0
5	1 0 1
6	1 1 0

1 indicated by a LED illuminated

0 indicated by a LED not illuminated

The switch used is a 2 pole 6 way type.

The circuit can be extended if a switch with more than 6 positions is available, with 4 LEDs in use the maximum count is 1111 which corresponds to 15, although as switches are not usually available for more than 12 way the maximum count possible will be 1100 (12).

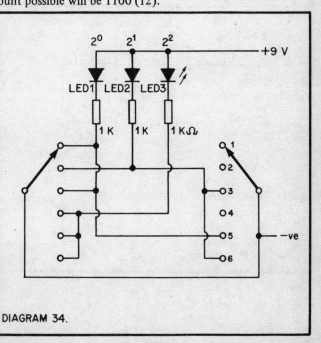

DIAGRAM 34.

CIRCUIT THIRTY-FIVE

LED NIGHTLIGHT

This is a LED circuit for a nightlight. When switched on the red LED glows brightly and then gradually dims over a period of about 30 minutes until the LED is extinguished. The time delay depends on the time taken for C1 to charge up, a higher value for C1 will give a longer time period. The transistors used are silicon NPN types such as the BC108.

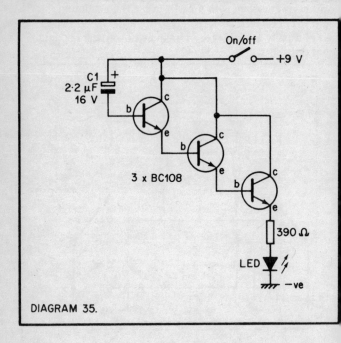

DIAGRAM 35.

CIRCUIT THIRTY-SIX

IC LED FLASHER

This circuit uses the logic gates of a 7400 type integrated circuit to form a low frequency multivibrator which drives two red LEDs causing them to flash alternately.

Each 7400 IC contains 4 gates sufficient to drive 4 red LEDs, the circuit diagram shows the circuit for one multivibrator,

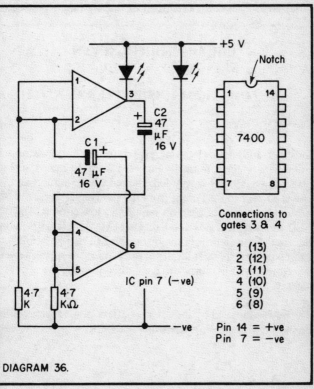

DIAGRAM 36.

the other 2 gates can also be connected together in similar fashion to form a second multivibrator. The pin numbers on the diagram are the connections to the 14 pin IC, the numbers given in brackets are the connections to the other 2 gates. The circuit should be powered from a 5 volt supply, although a 4½ volt battery can be used. The time interval between flashes depends on the volume of C1 and C2, for a longer time period (lower frequency) i.e. slower flashing rate a larger value of electrolytic capacitor e.g. 100µF or 220µF can be used.

If several 7400 ICs each driving 4 LEDs are assembled together with different values of timing capacitors used to give a variation in flash rates, a scintillating display can be produced.

CIRCUIT THIRTY-SEVEN

AUTOMATIC MAINS/BATTERY SWITCH

This is an automatic electronic switch for use in transistorised equipment which is normally powered from the mains. If the mains derived 9 volt supply fails the red LED conducts and passes current to the circuit from the reserve battery, note that it is only suitable for a circuit requiring a low current. The LED conducts and glows to indicate MAINS FAILURE. With the circuit powered from the mains the LED is reverse biased and no current flows from the battery, once the mains power is restored the LED turns off again disconnecting the reserve battery.

The power supplied by the reserve battery is less than 9 volts due to the voltage drop across the red LED.

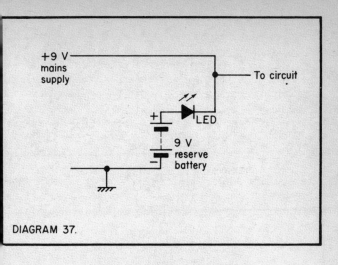

+9 V mains supply

To circuit

LED

9 V reserve battery

DIAGRAM 37.

CIRCUIT THIRTY-EIGHT

VOLTAGE COMPARATOR

This circuit uses a differential amplifier to compare 2 voltage inputs, if the 2 inputs are of equal voltage the 2 LEDs will be at equal brilliance. The light output varies between LEDs and so LED 1 and LED 2 should be matched for brilliance if possible.

The circuit can form the basis of an FM tuning indicator, one input can be an AFC reference voltage, the other input will be from the ratio discriminator output. The circuit is then adjusted so that at the optimum tuning point the two LEDs are of equal brilliance.

The two transistors used are silicon NPN types such as BC108. The two transistors used in the circuit should be a matched pair if possible.

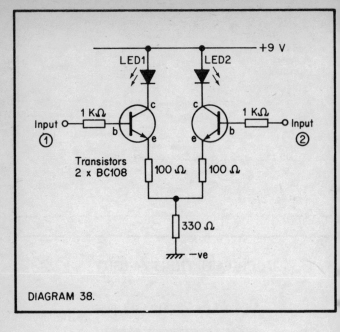

DIAGRAM 38.

CIRCUIT THIRTY-NINE

LED/ZENER VOLTAGE MEASURING

A LED and a zener diode connected in series can be used to measure a voltage.

For example if a red LED is connected in series with a 7.5 volt zener diode the combination will not conduct until the voltage exceeds 1.5v + 7.5v = 9 volts, i.e. the LED will not glow at all until the voltage exceeds 9 volts.

The 1KΩ resistor limits the current through the LED/zener combination.

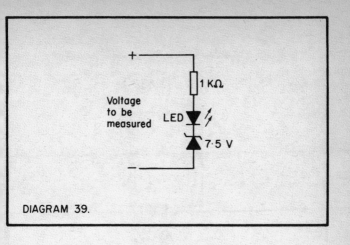

DIAGRAM 39.

CIRCUIT FORTY

LED/ZENER VOLTAGE RANGE MEASURING CIRCUIT

This circuit is a development of circuit (39). In circuit (39) when the red LED glows this is an indication that the voltage input exceeds the voltage drop across the LED/zener combination. If silicon rectifiers (type 1N4001) are added in parallel across the red LED, when the voltage across the LED exceeds 2.2 volts, the silicon rectifiers conduct and, due to the much lower forward resistance of a silicon rectifier compared to a LED, extinguishes the LED.

Circuit (40) uses a 10 volt zener and red LED combination so that the LED glows at 11.5 (10 + 1.5v) and is extinguished at 12.2v (10 + 2.2v), so that if the LED is glowing it indicates the voltage is between 11.5 and 12.2 volts.

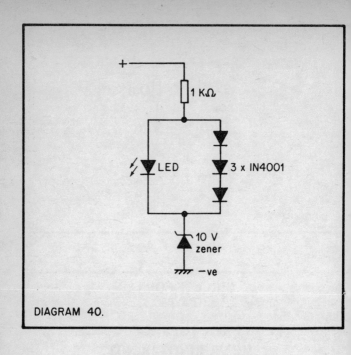

DIAGRAM 40.

CIRCUIT FORTY-ONE

CONSTANT CURRENT CHARGER

A LED has a constant voltage drop across it when under forward bias, this constant voltage can be used as a reference for a transistor in a current control circuit. In circuit (41) a small transistor supplies a constant current of 50mA which is sufficient to recharge small Nickel-Cadmium cells. The 2N697 transistor should be fitted with a TO5 type heat-sink as it will be passing current for several hours while recharging Ni-Cad cells. With a 9 volt input as indicated one, two or three Ni-Cad cells can be recharged.

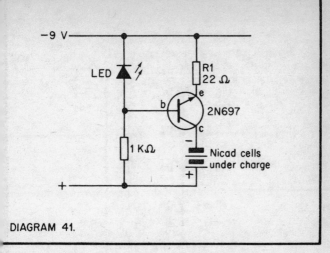

DIAGRAM 41.

The current flow is controlled by the transistor, the current is set by the value of R1, if R1 is 22Ω, the current is fixed at 50mA. If a lower current is required the value of R1 should be increased e.g. for 25mA R1 should be 39Ω.

If a higher current is required a lower value for R1 is required but in this case a higher power rating transistor should be used.

CIRCUIT FORTY-TWO

MULTIZENER

This circuit depends on connecting LEDs, rectifiers and zener diodes in combination to form voltage regulators. It is also a use of the binary system. The switches shown in the circuit diagram are SPST types, when the switch is in the OFF position the diodes controlled by that switch are in circuit, when the switch is in the ON position the diodes are bypassed.

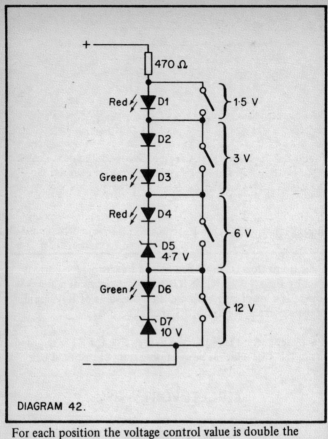

DIAGRAM 42.

For each position the voltage control value is double the previous section. The first "element" is a red LED which gives a voltage drop of 1½ volts, the next element is a green LED and a silicon rectifier in series which gives a total voltage drop of nearly 3 volts (2.2 volts + 0.75 volts) as the forward voltage drops across a green LED is about 2.2 volts.

The next element is a red LED + a 4.7v zener diode. Total voltage 1.5v + 4.7v = 6.2 volts.

The final element is a green LED + 10v zener diode, voltage

50

10v + 2.2v = 12.2v. The total set gives a close approximation to the binary series 1½v, 3v, 6v, 12 volt.

When in use each LED glows to indicate when in circuit; by use of the four switches any voltage from 1½v to 22½v (1½ + 3 + 6 + 12) can be regulated.

The voltages available are 1½v, 3v, 4½v, 6v, 7½v, 9v, 10½v. 12v, 13½v, 15v, 16½v, 18v, 19½v, 21v and 22½v.

If required the binary series can be extended, the next element is 24 volts, this could be a green LED + a 22 volt zener diode. The zener diodes used in the circuit can be 400mW types.

The multizener is intended for low power reference voltage purposes only, if high power regulation is required the multizener should be used to provide the control voltage for a power transistor.

Components List

D1, D4	Red LED
D3, D6	Green LED
D2	1N4001 silicon rectifier
D5	4.7v ⎤ 400mW zener diode
D6	10v ⎦

CIRCUIT FORTY-THREE

DUAL VOLTAGE REGULATOR

This is a transistor voltage regulator designed for a 12 volt input. The reference voltage for the 2N697 transistor is provided by LED/zener combinations, the rectifier compensates for the voltage drop across the transistor. The current supplied by the regulator should be less than 100mA, if a higher current is required a larger transistor

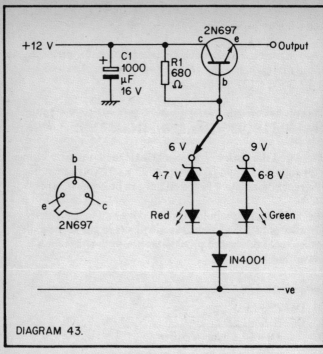

DIAGRAM 43.

such as a 2N3055 should be substituted. The voltages supplied are 6.2v (1.5v + 4.7v) and 9v (2.2v + 6.8v) the LEDs indicate which voltage the regulator is switched to, red 6.2 volts, green 9 volts. The switch used can be a SPDT slide type.

Components List

R1   Resistor 680Ω ½W
D1   4.7v 400mW zener
D2   Red LED
D3   1n4001 silicon rectifier
D4   6.8v 400mW zener
D5   Green LED
Transistor 2N697
C1   1000μF 16v electrolytic capacitor

CIRCUIT FORTY-FOUR

LOW VOLTAGE TESTER

This is a very simple two red LED circuit to test low voltages. The 2 LEDs and the resistor are fitted inside a small plastic box equipped with 2 flying test leads. LED 1 is fitted next to lead 1, LED 2 is fitted next to lead 2.

In use, the 2 leads are connected to the low voltage circuit under test, the red LED glow indicates positive. If LED 1 glows this indicates that lead 1 is connected to the positive line (lead 2 negative), if LED 2 glows this indicates that lead 2 is connected to the positive line (lead 1 negative). If both LEDs glow this indicates that the voltage under test is AC.

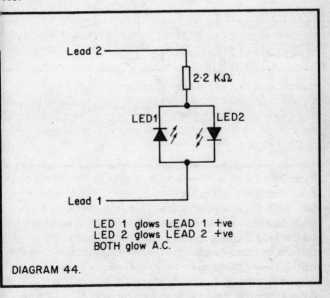

LED 1 glows LEAD 1 +ve
LED 2 glows LEAD 2 +ve
BOTH glow A.C.

DIAGRAM 44.

CIRCUIT FORTY-FIVE

OPTICALLY ISOLATED
VARIABLE RESISTANCE

This is a circuit for the experimenter. The light from a red LED
is allowed to fall onto an ORP12 or similar cadmium sulphide
photoconductive cell. The cadmium sulphide cell has a resistance in the dark (i.e. no light on it) of several million ohms,
under very bright conditions the resistance may fall to a few
hundred ohms or less, so that a wide range of resistance is
possible.

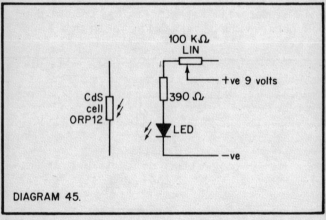

DIAGRAM 45.

In use the LED should be positioned next to the ORP12 cell,
some adjustment will be required to find the most sensitive
spot. While the adjustments are carried out the ORP12 cell
should be connected to the low ohms range of a multimeter
and the LED should be set at maximum brilliance, the
positions can then be adjusted for minimum resistance of the
ORP12. Once the optimum position has been found the two
components should be shielded from ambient lighting. In the
prototype circuit the LED was glued onto the ORP12 with

transparent polystyrene cement, both were then wrapped in black insulating tape. In use the variable resistor controls the brightness of the LED and the brightness of the LED controls the resistance of the ORP12.

If the circuit is required for a "noiseless" volume control the supply to the LED should be very well smoothed to avoid the LED light output being modulated by mains hum due to ripple on the power supply. The circuit has the great advantage that the ORP12 is completely isolated from the electrical circuit controlling the LED, there is no electrical connection.

CIRCUIT FORTY-SIX

THREE LED PRESET STATION INDICATOR

This is an indicator circuit for use with an FM tuner using preset tuning. The preset system requires a six push buttom switch for selection of six FM stations. Each push button controls 3 ganged ON/OFF switches so that each position must have 3 pole on/off or switching that can be used in this way, e.g. 3 pole 2 way. Most pushbutton assemblies have more switching capability than shown in the diagram, any surplus positions are left unconnected. For each position of switching one of the ON/OFF switches connects in the preset voltage for the FM varicap tuner system, the remaining two switches control the three LEDs. The indication is based on the binary system of counting, diagram 46(a) illustrates how the various LEDs glow to indicate each station.

Note that as a six position switch is used one combination is unused. LED 1, 2, and 3 illuminated this corresponds to a seventh station i.e. binary equivalent of seven.

Diagram 46(b) illustrates the connections to the switches the poles of the switches are numbered 1A, 1B, 1C, 2A etc. the C poles of the switches control the selection of preset voltages for tuning.

WHITE SPOT LED GLOWING, BLACK SPOT LED OFF.

LED 3	LED 2	LED 1	STATION
●	●	○	ONE
●	○	●	TWO
●	○	○	THREE
○	●	●	FOUR
○	●	○	FIVE
○	○	●	SIX

DIAGRAM 46 (a)

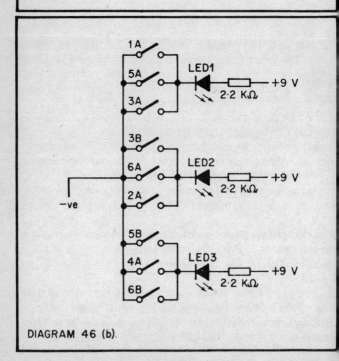

DIAGRAM 46 (b).

SWITCH 1 a, b, c is for station 1
SWITCH 2 a, b, c is for station 2 etc.

In the original prototype FM tuner a pleasing layout was obtained by using SIX LEDs, LEDs 1, 2, 3 on the left hand side of the front panel comprised the station indicator, LEDs 4, 5 and 6 were on the right hand side of the front panel. LEDs 4 and 6 were used in a 2 LED tuning indicator and LED 5 was used as the stereo beacon, this gave a pleasing symmetrical design.

THE 707 COMMON ANODE DISPLAY

The 707 display consists of 8 LEDs forming the seven segments, A, B, C, D, E, F, G and the decimal point by illumination of the various segments all the numbers 0, 1, 2, 3, 4, 5, 6, 7, 8, 9 can be displayed.

The 707 is housed in a 14 DIL package pins 4, 5 and 12 are missing.

CIRCUIT FORTY-SEVEN

RANDOM NUMBER DISPLAY

This circuit uses a 707 common anode LED display, which consists of 8 LEDs with a common anode connection and 8 separate cathode connections, the eighth LED is for the decimal point.

If two 7400 IC multivibrators are constructed, the eight LEDs are required (see circuit 36) can be the eight LEDs of a seven segment display. The LEDs will flash on and off and

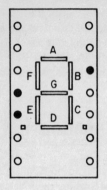

707 display

PIN 1 cathode A
PIN 2 cathode F
PIN 3 common ANODE
PIN 6 cathode D.P.
PIN 7 cathode E
PIN 8 cathode D
PIN 10 cathode C
PIN 11 cathode G
PIN 13 cathode B

DL707 common anode display
14 D.I.L. pins 3, 4, 5, 12 missing

DIAGRAM 47.

certain combinations form numbers. A more effective display
is possible if two 707 displays and eight multivibrators using
four 7400 ICs are connected together.

Each multivibrator has two outputs A and $\overline{A}$, i.e. if one output is ON the other is off. If each A output is connected to
one 7 segment display and the $\overline{A}$ outputs are connected to
the other, the most effective display is produced. If all the
LEDs on one 707 display are "on" the display reads .8,
the other display is blank, if one display reads 1 the other
reads 3. The displays will be constantly changing because
even if all the multivibrators have identical capacitors, due
to the variation in nominal capacitor values, each one will
run at a slightly different rate.

CIRCUIT FORTY-EIGHT

LEGEND DISPLAY

The 707 display can be used as a legend display by connecting
the various cathodes together. Circuit (48) depicts the display
used as a stereo beacon for a stereo decoder, the cathodes are
connected together to display 5 which looks like and S for
STEREO.

An alternative display is to use segments A and D as the two
LEDs in a 2 LED tuning indicator, and use segments F, G and
C as the stereo beacon LEDs, when a station is on tune the
two segments will be illuminated, if the station is transmitting
in stereo, the 2 segments together with the 3 segments
illuminated by the decoder form a 5 or S.

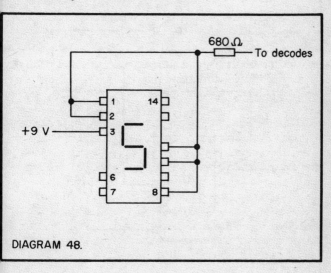

DIAGRAM 48.

The 707 display by suitable interconnections can display.

1 or I	6 or G
2	7
3	8 or B
4 or H	9
5 or S	0 or O

also A, C, E, F, H, L, P, U and with the decimal point,
.1, .2, .3, .4, .5, .6, .7, .8, .9, .0.

CIRCUIT FORTY-NINE

ROMAN 1, 2, 3 DISPLAY

This is a very simple circuit to enable the Roman figures I, II
and III to be displayed for circuit indication. A 707 display
is mounted sideways the switch turns on the segments D, G
and A in turn.

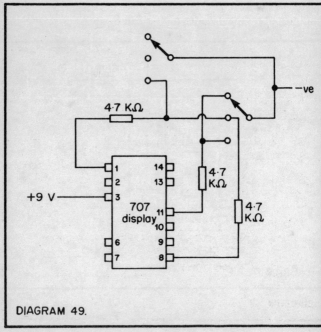

DIAGRAM 49.

I   is segment G on
II   is segments D and A on
III   is segments D, A and G on.

The segments are controlled by a 2 pole 3 way switch, spare poles of the switch can be used to control the circuits so numbered.

CIRCUIT FIFTY

NUMERICAL DISPLAY

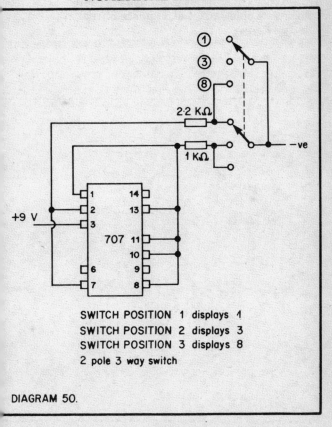

SWITCH POSITION 1 displays 1
SWITCH POSITION 2 displays 3
SWITCH POSITION 3 displays 8
2 pole 3 way switch

DIAGRAM 50.

The 707 display can with the use of switching display several numbers in turn. The switching is simplified if the numbers have common segments. For example a circuit to display 8 or 9 is very simple the difference is segment E, only this needs to be switched ON and OFF to change the number. If segment ABCDFG are continuously on and E off 9 is displayed, if E is on an 8 is displayed. Other examples are 5 and 6 this pair of numbers differ in one segment only.

The circuit shown in diagram fifty displays 1, 3 or 8; 1 and 3 have no common segments which simplifies switching, when both sets are displayed 1 and 3 form an 8. The switch is a 2 pole 3 way type.

OTHER BOOKS OF INTEREST

BP36: 50 CIRCUITS USING GERMANIUM SILICON AND ZENEF DIODES
R.N. Soar
ISBN: 0 89534 039 2 £1.5(
Approx. Size: 178 x 111 mm *64 page*

Contains 50 interesting and useful circuits and applications, coverin many different branches of electronics, using one of the most simple an(inexpensive of components — the diode. Includes the use of germaniun and silicon signal diodes, silicon rectifier diodes and zener diodes, etc. A valuable addition to the library of both the beginner and more advance(enthusiast alike.

BP87: 50 SIMPLE L.E.D. CIRCUITS – BOOK 2
R.N. Soar
ISBN: 0 85934 062 7 £1.3!
Approx. Size: 178 x 111 mm *64 page.*

In this book the author has devised and developed a further series o useful applications and circuits, covering many different branches o electronics, using the simple Light Emitting Diode (L.E.D.). These in n(way supercede or replace those published in the original book (BP42 but complement them, offering many more ideas to the reader.